ELEVEN PLUS

VERBAL REASONING

PRACTICE PAPERS 9 to 12

A	F	N
Publishing		

AFN Publishing Ltd

www.afnpublishing.co.uk

First published in Great Britain in 2008 by:

AFN Publishing Ltd
PO Box 1558
Gerrards Cross
Buckinghamshire
SL9 0XL

www.afnpublishing.co.uk

ISBN 978-0-9538487-7-5

Guidance Notes for Parents

The Practice Papers in this book are designed to introduce children to the types of questions found on eleven plus secondary school selection tests and to help develop techniques for answering them.

It is important that your child's confidence is developed by working through the Practice Papers and the approach suggested below will help to achieve this. If your child has completed Practice Papers 1 to 4 or Practice Papers 5 to 8 then the approach for Practice Paper 12 should be used for all the Practice Papers in this book.

The Progress Record at the back of the book can be used to monitor your child's progress.

Practice Paper 9

Read through the instructions on the Practice Paper with your child and explain what is required. It is recommended that you work through the first Practice Paper with your child <u>without timing</u> the exercise. Whilst working through the Practice Paper explain what the questions are asking you to do and what techniques should be used to answer them. You do not necessarily need to go through the whole Practice Paper at one time and you may want to divide the Practice Paper, so that it can be covered in more manageable sessions.

Practice Paper 10

Let your child work through the second Practice Paper alone, <u>again without timing</u>. However, ensure that you are available to answer queries and to help if your child gets stuck on a particular type of question. After marking the Practice Paper, go through any questions that your child has got wrong and explain how they should have been answered. Explain the technique again and ensure that your child understands what the question is asking for. Remember to give recognition for correct answers.

Practice Paper 11

For Practice Paper 11 you should time your child. Encourage your child not to spend too much time on any one question but to keep up the momentum by leaving out questions that he or she is unsure of. Missed questions can be returned to at the end, if there is time.

After 50 minutes draw a line to show how far through the Practice Paper your child managed to get. This will allow you to identify how many questions your child was able to answer in the time available. However, let your child continue to the end of the Practice Paper before marking it.

After marking the Practice Paper, review the techniques used to answer the questions with your child to identify whether any improvements can be made.

Practice Paper 12

The aim of Practice Paper 12 should be to practise technique and to increase your child's accuracy and speed. You should therefore time this Practice Paper and encourage your child to monitor the time so that they are aware of their own progress - this will be very important in the actual examinations.

After 50 minutes draw a line underneath the last question your child has answered so that you know how far he or she managed to get in the time allowed. After drawing the line, allow your child to complete the Practice Paper.

When you have marked the Practice Paper, work through any questions that your child has answered incorrectly and review the technique used. Remember to provide recognition for overall effort and correct answers.

If your child needs more exercises, Practice Papers 1 to 4 and Practice Papers 5 to 8 are available in traditional format (ISBN 0-9538487-3-6 and 0-9538487-5-2) and multiple-choice format (ISBN 0-9538487-1-X and 0-9538487-4-4). Additional questions can also be found in our Eleven Plus Verbal Reasoning Techniques & Practice Questions book (ISBN 0-9538487-2-8) which also explains how to answer the questions. Details of these, and other publications, can be found at **www.afnpublishing.co.uk**

Practice Paper 9

(Verbal Reasoning)

Please read the following before you start the Practice Paper:

1. Do not begin the Practice Paper until you are told to do so.

2. The Practice Paper contains 80 questions and you have 50 minutes to complete it.

3. Read the questions carefully so that you know what to do.

4. Mark your answers clearly using a <u>pencil</u>.

5. If you want to change one of your answers, rub out the wrong answer completely and enter the new answer. <u>Do not cross out any answers</u>.

6. Try and answer as many questions as you can. You may not be able to answer all of them, so if you cannot answer a question go on to the next one. Do not spend too much time on one question.

7. When you get to the end of the Practice Paper, go back and check your answers.

This Practice Paper is printed using blue ink - if the writing isn't blue it is an illegal copy

In the sentences below you must find a **four-letter** word that is hidden at the end of one word and the start of the next word. You must not change the order of the letters.

Example: The guar<u>d ent</u>ered the building silently.

1. The robber stole all the jewels.

2. They work in the same shop.

3. The guest arrived at the party.

4. The girl left the door open.

5. When should we leave for school?

6. The boy liked fish and chips.

In the questions below you must move one letter from the word on the left to the word on the right to make two new words. You are only allowed to move one letter and must not re-arrange any of the other letters.

Example: PART   LANE   [Art   ]   [Plane]

7. FOLD   SCAR   [   ]   [   ]

8. PRICE   ART   [   ]   [   ]

9. ARCH   EAR   [   ]   [   ]

10. MOTHER   TRAP   [   ]   [   ]

11. GOAT   ROD   [   ]   [   ]

12. BROWN   EAT   [   ]   [   ]

PLEASE CONTINUE ON THE NEXT PAGE

In the questions below find **two** words, one from each group, that are **similar** in meaning.

Example: [start, loud, fold]   [begin, quiet, hungry]

13.   [wait, destroy, face]   [break, low, tired]

14.   [exit, worry, bright]   [happy, wild, leave]

15.   [timid, dry, right]   [wool, shy, hurry]

16.   [push, great, buy]   [purchase, knot, boast]

17.   [place, home, fast]   [tape, quick, water]

18.   [wet, bake, steal]   [ride, parent, soaked]

In these questions find **two** words, one from each group, which make a new word when combined. The word from the group on the left must come first.

Example: [grow, part, wise]   [ridge, slope, bounce]

19.   [star, lose, golf]   [ring, home, hump]

20.   [tar, raid, dare]   [fade, get, bold]

21.   [jam, haste, deter]   [bolt, mine, door]

22.   [start, grate, pole]   [fully, wise, port]

23.   [beak, crane, bar]   [wish, wake, row]

24.   [stop, arm, will]   [dome, even, ping]

PLEASE CONTINUE ON THE NEXT PAGE

In the following questions numbers have been replaced with letters. You need to work out the answers to the sums.

Example: If A = 3, B = 4, C = 5 and D = 6. Calculate the answer to this sum **as a number:**

A + B + C = [**12**]

25. If A = 6, B = 4, C = 2 and D = 0

Calculate the answer to this sum **as a number:**

A + B + D = [   ]

26. If A = 10, B = 5, C = 4 and D = 1

Calculate the answer to this sum **as a letter:**

A - B - C = [   ]

27. If A = 2, B = 4, C = 6 and D = 8

Calculate the answer to this sum **as a letter:**

A x D ÷ B = [   ]

28. If A = 1, B = 5, C = 10 and D = 15

Calculate the answer to this sum **as a number:**

D - C - A = [   ]

29. If A = 3, B = 6, C = 9 and D = 12

Calculate the answer to this sum **as a number:**

A + B + C + D = [   ]

30. If A = 10, B = 5, C = 2 and D = 0

Calculate the answer to this sum **as a letter:**

A x B x D = [   ]

PLEASE CONTINUE ON THE NEXT PAGE

There are four words and three code numbers written below. The codes are in a different order to the words and one code is missing.

READ   DARE   PEAR   FORD
    4326   6325   1765

31. What is the code number for DEER?

32. What is the code number for FARE?

33. Which word has the code number 6263?

34. What is the code number for DROP?

35. Which word has the code number 4675?

36. What is the code number for FADE?

In the following questions the underlined word has had three consecutive letters removed. These three letters make a word without being rearranged. What is the three-letter word?

Example: Some shops are closed on day.   [Sun   ]

37. The besmaids arrived at church.   [   ]

38. There was silence when the teac entered the classroom. [   ]

39. She put a new cridge in her fountain pen.   [   ]

40. Please could I bor a ruler?   [   ]

41. The volo spewed lava into the air.   [   ]

42. A mahon is 26 miles and 385 yards long.   [   ]

PLEASE CONTINUE ON THE NEXT PAGE

43. Anthony, Pablo and Harry need to be able to throw a ball more than 30 metres to get a certificate from their school.

Anthony and Pablo can throw a ball more than 30 metres.

Harry can throw a ball further than Anthony and Pablo.

Which one of the following must be true?

A. Anthony can throw a ball further than Pablo.

B. Harry cannot get a certificate.

C. Anthony, Pablo and Harry are able to get certificates.

D. No one receives a certificate.

E. Pablo can throw a ball further than Harry.

In the following questions some of the words have been written in code. In each question the code has been "broken" for one word. You must use the same code to work out the second word.

A B C D E F G H I J K L M N O P Q R S T U V W X Y Z

Example: If SJDF means RICE, what does SPTF mean? [ROSE   ]

44. If YKNF means WILD,
what does OWUV mean? [   ]

45. If VHRD is the code for WISE,
what is the code for LOST? [   ]

46. If GCUQ means FARM,
what does LPRX mean? [   ]

47. If HLIA is the code for HOLD,
what is the code for STOP? [   ]

48. If DSGB means BOAT,
what does ESRL mean? [   ]

49. If KBOM is the code for HELP,
what is the code for NOSE? [   ]

PLEASE CONTINUE ON THE NEXT PAGE

Using the alphabet shown below identify the next letters in the sequences.

A B C D E F G H I J K L M N O P Q R S T U V W X Y Z

Example: BZ,   CY,   DX,   EW,   [FV]

50. EG,   GH,   II,   KJ,   [   ]

51. RD,   PF,   NH,   LJ,   [   ]

52. RR,   SN,   TJ,   UF,   [   ]

53. AZ,   BX,   DV,   GT,   KR,   [   ]

54. FY,   HX,   JV,   LS,   NO,   [   ]

55. KL,   KM,   LK,   LN,   MJ,   [   ]

In the questions below find a letter that goes at the end of one word and the start of the other. The **same** letter must fit in both sets of brackets.

Example: wil [d] eal   bal [d   ] oom

56.   whe [   ] ewt   wor [   ] ext

57.   ben [   ] ent   mee [   ] old

58.   arc [   ] elp   ras [   ] eel

59.   ban [   ] oal   lon [   ] reen

60.   tea [   ] ace   roa [   ] ear

61.   lea [   ] arm   ree [   ] air

PLEASE CONTINUE ON THE NEXT PAGE

In the following questions calculate the number that will complete each sum.

Example: 6 + 4 = 5 + ?   [5   ]

62. 4 + 8 = 10 + ?   [   ]

63. 20 - 9 = 9 + ?   [   ]

64. 6 x 5 = 2 x 10 + ?   [   ]

65. 8 + 3 - 5 = 9 + 4 - ?   [   ]

66. 20 ÷ 5 = 2 x 2 + ?   [   ]

67. 100 ÷ 10 x 2 = ? + 4   [   ]

In the questions below find the number that continues the sequence.

Example: 2, 4, 6, 8,   [10   ]

68. 3, 6, 9, 12,   [   ]

69. 32, 16, 8, 4, 2,   [   ]

70. 25, 20, 15, 10,   [   ]

71. 16, 14, 12, 10,   [   ]

72. 25, 20, 16, 13,   [   ]

73. 3, 1, 6, 2, 9, 3,   [   ]

PLEASE CONTINUE ON THE NEXT PAGE

In these questions there are two groups of words. The word in the left-hand brackets has been formed in a certain way using letters from the other words on the left-hand side. Use the letters in the words on the right-hand side to form a word **in the same way**.

Example: LAST [STOP] OPEN : RARE [REAR] ARCH

74.   FEED [FOLD] BOLT   :   HOLD [   ] BEAK

75.   RACE [ACID] IDEA   :   BARK [   ] CHEW

76.   WORM [ROOM] MOVE   :   POSE [   ] PULP

77.   CREEK [KEEP] SPARE   :   STAFF [   ] AMBER

78.   LEAK [LEAD] DEAL   :   BEAR [   ] DOVE

79.   PARK [RAKE] LACE   :   FARM [   ] CAMP

80.   Natasha, Lorraine and Martin study Chemistry, English and Mathematics.

Kirsten and Monica both study Spanish and History.

Natasha and Martin study Biology and French.

Lorraine studies Physics and IT.

Martin and Lorraine study Geography.

Martin studies Drama.

Who is studying the most subjects?

THIS IS THE END OF THE TEST

Practice Paper 10

(Verbal Reasoning)

Please read the following before you start the Practice Paper:

1. Do not begin the Practice Paper until you are told to do so.

2. The Practice Paper contains 80 questions and you have 50 minutes to complete it.

3. Read the questions carefully so that you know what to do.

4. Mark your answers clearly using a <u>pencil</u>.

5. If you want to change one of your answers, rub out the wrong answer completely and enter the new answer. <u>Do not cross out any answers</u>.

6. Try and answer as many questions as you can. You may not be able to answer all of them, so if you cannot answer a question go on to the next one. Do not spend too much time on one question.

7. When you get to the end of the Practice Paper, go back and check your answers.

This Practice Paper is printed using blue ink - if the writing isn't blue it is an illegal copy

In the questions below there are two sets of words. Find a word that goes equally well with both sets.

Example: [smash, destroy]   [stop, cease]   [break   ]

1.   [spring, waterhole]   [fit, healthy]   [   ]

2.   [brilliant, dazzling]   [clever, intelligent]   [   ]

3.   [pit, colliery]   [explosive, bomb]   [   ]

4.   [container, chest]   [fight, spar]   [   ]

5.   [coil, spiral]   [pounce, bounce]   [   ]

6.   [ring, hoop]   [orchestra, group]   [   ]

In these questions find one word from each pair of brackets that will complete the sentence in the most sensible way.

Example: Knife is to [rust, dog, fork] as bat is to [ball, crisp, tree].

7.   Wild is to [pleased, jump, tame] as old is to [oldest, new, clean].

8.   Write is to [went, funny, right] as pale is to [middle, foot, pail].

9.   Paris is to [Belgium, France, England] as Berlin is to [Germany, Spain, Italy].

10.   Clown is to [circus, funny, laugh] as chef is to [oven, kitchen, spoon].

11.   High is to [wide, small, highest] as fast is to [fastest, slowest, quick].

12.   Flew is to [fly, bird, flu] as saw is to [sea, see, watch].

PLEASE CONTINUE ON THE NEXT PAGE

In the following questions the pairs of letters are related in the same way. Use the alphabet shown below to work out the missing letters.

A B C D E F G H I J K L M N O P Q R S T U V W X Y Z

Example: AX is related to BW as FV is related to   [GU   ]

13. FX is related to GY as RB is related to   [   ]

14. NQ is related to SO as ML is related to   [   ]

15. VF is related to XI as EO is related to   [   ]

16. WE is related to UG as KT is related to   [   ]

17. DZ is related to DP as LQ is related to   [   ]

18. UX is related to YY as CN is related to   [   ]

In the following questions there are three pairs of words. The second word in each pair of brackets has been formed in the **same way** by using letters from the first word in the brackets.

Find the word that completes the last pair of words.

Example: [peat   pea]   [note   not]   [cane   **can**]

19. [barb   bar]   [been   bee]   [cart   ?]

20. [fold   old]   [star   tar]   [tall   ?]

21. [greet   tee]   [notes   set]   [bonus   ?]

22. [stamps   tap]   [though   hog]   [spider   ?]

23. [wanted   ten]   [siphon   hop]   [tended   ?]

24. [twitch   wit]   [sparks   par]   [folded   ?]

PLEASE CONTINUE ON THE NEXT PAGE

In the following questions find **two** words that are **different** from the others.

Example: [rose, daisy, <u>beech</u>, snowdrop, <u>oak</u>]

25. [cow, ewe, bull, sow, drake]

26. [peach, grape, raspberry, orange, apple]

27. [house, mansion, road, garden, flat]

28. [pen, paper, pencil, chalk, envelope]

29. [letter, magazine, book, television, radio]

30. [ancient, old, immense, huge, massive]

31. Ruth, James and Olivia need £4 each to buy a magazine.

James has £3.95.

Ruth and Olivia both have more money than James.

Which one of the following must be true?

A. Ruth and Olivia have enough money to each buy a magazine.

B. James borrows some money so that he can buy a magazine.

C. James doesn't buy a magazine.

D. Ruth has more money than Olivia.

E. Ruth, James and Olivia all buy a magazine.

PLEASE CONTINUE ON THE NEXT PAGE

In these questions the three numbers in each group are related in exactly the same way. Calculate the number to complete the third group.

Example: (6 [10] 4)   (2 [5] 3)   (1 [7] 6)

32. (6 [14] 8)   (3 [6] 3)   (7 [   ] 6)

33. (1 [7] 8)   (3 [7] 10)   (4 [   ] 9)

34. (4 [24] 6)   (6 [12] 2)   (9 [   ] 2)

35. (3 [3] 9)   (4 [5] 20)   (3 [   ] 12)

36. (11 [10] 21)   (2 [10] 12)   (90 [   ] 100)

37. (15 [17] 1)   (8 [12] 3)   (9 [   ] 2)

In the questions below find **two** words, one from each group, that are **opposite** in meaning.

Example: [wise, brave, told]   [grave, spare, foolish]

38. [bright, fix, jest]   [shiny, dull, drink]

39. [late, happy, moan]   [clever, punctual, worry]

40. [wriggle, fastest, most]   [slow, grand, slowest]

41. [commence, top, deny]   [complete, witness, silly]

42. [help, note, messy]   [modern, hinder, grumpy]

43. [solid, cheap, cheep]   [expensive, more, stop]

PLEASE CONTINUE ON THE NEXT PAGE

44. Mandy, Louise, Dave and Alison each have a bicycle.

    Dave, and Louise also have a scooter.

    Dave owns some rollerblades.

    Mandy, Louise and Alison have a skateboard.

    Alison and Dave each own a pogo stick.

    Fred has a tricycle.

    Who has the most toys?

In the questions below find a letter that goes at the end of one word and the start of the other. The **same** letter must fit in both sets of brackets.

Example: hop [e] ven   har [e] nds

45.   ste [   ] ear   lea [   ] est

46.   boa [   ] eal   nea [   ] ell

47.   bes [   ] ell   soo [   ] alk

48.   spa [   ] oon   bea [   ] ose

49.   ric [   ] asy   hom [   ] ach

50.   plo [   ] aze   rea [   ] eck

PLEASE CONTINUE ON THE NEXT PAGE

In the following questions numbers have been replaced with letters. You need to work out the answers to the sums.

Example: If A = 1, B = 2, C = 3 and D = 4. Calculate the answer to this sum **as a number:**

A + B + D = [7]

51. If A = 3, B = 4, C = 5 and D = 6

    Calculate the answer to this sum **as a number:**

    A + B + D = [   ]

52. If A = 2, B = 4, C = 8 and D = 16

    Calculate the answer to this sum **as a letter:**

    C - B - A = [   ]

53. If A = 8, B = 6, C = 4 and D = 2

    Calculate the answer to this sum **as a number:**

    A x C ÷ D = [   ]

54. If A = 15, B = 10, C = 5 and D = 0

    Calculate the answer to this sum **as a letter:**

    A - C - D = [   ]

55. If A = 14, B = 7, C = 10 and D = 8

    Calculate the answer to this sum **as a number:**

    A ÷ B x C = [   ]

56. If A = 1, B = 3, C = 5 and D = 15

    Calculate the answer to this sum **as a letter:**

    A x B x C = [   ]

PLEASE CONTINUE ON THE NEXT PAGE

In the following questions the underlined word has had three consecutive letters removed. These three letters make a word without being rearranged. What is the three-letter word?

Example: What time does the examination <u>st</u>?   [art   ]

57.   I'm going to a football match on <u>urday</u>.   [   ]

58.   The <u>polman</u> arrested the criminals.   [   ]

59.   The snake <u>shered</u> along the ground.   [   ]

60.   The <u>cls</u> at the circus were very funny.   [   ]

61.   The postman delivered the <u>ters</u>.   [   ]

62.   I don't eat <u>bage</u>, cauliflower or broccoli.   [   ]

In the questions below find the number that continues the sequence.

Example: 1, 3, 5, 7,   [9]

63.   16, 20, 24, 28,   [   ]

64.   20, 18, 16, 14, 12,   [   ]

65.   9, 12, 15, 18,   [   ]

66.   3, 6, 12, 24,   [   ]

67.   2, 10, 4, 9, 6, 8,   [   ]

68.   10, 3, 8, 6, 6,   [   ]

PLEASE CONTINUE ON THE NEXT PAGE

In the sentences below you must find a **four-letter** word that is hidden at the end of one word and the start of the next word. You must not change the order of the letters.

Example: The soldier marched towards <u>the ro</u>ad.

69. He could not answer the question.

70. They escaped from the prison camp.

71. The coach allowed them to continue.

72. She ate two bars of chocolate.

73. Please will you follow after them?

74. What shall we do after lunch?

In these questions find **two** words, one from each group, which make a new word when combined. The word from the group on the left must come first.

Example: [bang, <u>spar</u>, fold]   [<u>row</u>, rant, help]

75. [rub, tug, mat]   [bed, other, dice]

76. [led, roof, slip]   [fade, get, per]

77. [all, has, bounce]   [net, ten, low]

78. [mar, best, yak]   [row, post, hot]

79. [just, woo, dock]   [wish, den, not]

80. [shop, wet, hit]   [dent, ping, pan]

THIS IS THE END OF THE TEST

Practice Paper 11

(Verbal Reasoning)

Please read the following before you start the Practice Paper:

1. Do not begin the Practice Paper until you are told to do so.

2. The Practice Paper contains 80 questions and you have 50 minutes to complete it.

3. Read the questions carefully so that you know what to do.

4. Mark your answers clearly using a <u>pencil</u>.

5. If you want to change one of your answers, rub out the wrong answer completely and enter the new answer. <u>Do not cross out any answers</u>.

6. Try and answer as many questions as you can. You may not be able to answer all of them, so if you cannot answer a question go on to the next one. Do not spend too much time on one question.

7. When you get to the end of the Practice Paper, go back and check your answers.

This Practice Paper is printed using blue ink - if the writing isn't blue it is an illegal copy

In these questions find **two** words, one from each group, which make a new word when combined. The word from the group on the left must come first.

Example: [taste, <u>bat</u>, grave]   [slip, wool, <u>her</u>]

1.   [bow, got, end]   [door, bold, led]

2.   [nose, bet, bike]   [ting, sad, help]

3.   [cart, bolt, beep]   [blue, fold, ridge]

4.   [fen, win, old]   [led, sing, king]

5.   [drop, fade, pea]   [den, wild, cock]

6.   [pull, red, last]   [over, got, post]

There are four words and three code numbers written below. The codes are in a different order to the words and one code is missing.

BEAK   DARK   BARE   READ
    5462   2651   3654

7.   What is the code number for BEAR?

8.   What is the code number for REEK?

9.   Which word has the code number 5654?

10.   What is the code number for DEAD?

11.   Which word has the code number 3651?

12.   What is the code number for DREAD?

PLEASE CONTINUE ON THE NEXT PAGE

In the following questions numbers have been replaced with letters. You need to work out the answers to the sums.

Example: If A = 2, B = 4, C = 6 and D = 8. Calculate the answer to this sum **as a number:**

A + B + D = [**14**]

13. If A = 1, B = 2, C = 3 and D = 4

   Calculate the answer to this sum **as a number:**

   A + C + D = [   ]

14. If A = 9, B = 6, C = 3 and D = 0

   Calculate the answer to this sum **as a letter:**

   A - B - D = [   ]

15. If A = 1, B = 2, C = 4 and D = 6

   Calculate the answer to this sum **as a number:**

   A x D x B = [   ]

16. If A = 5, B = 10, C = 15 and D = 20

   Calculate the answer to this sum **as a letter:**

   D - C + A = [   ]

17. If A = 3, B = 6, C = 9 and D = 12

   Calculate the answer to this sum **as a number:**

   A + B + C - D = [   ]

18. If A = 10, B = 5, C = 3 and D = 1

   Calculate the answer to this sum **as a number:**

   A x B x C = [   ]

PLEASE CONTINUE ON THE NEXT PAGE

In the questions below find a letter that goes at the end of one word and the start of the other. The **same** letter must fit in both sets of brackets.

Example: bar [k] oala   par [k] eep

19.   win [   ] ven   mor [   ] nds

20.   bea [   ] ear   fea [   ] ise

21.   hel [   ] ole   ste [   ] ork

22.   mon [   ] eep   tal [   ] nife

23.   spi [   ] ame   car [   ] ape

24.   far [   ] eat   pal [   ] oat

In the questions below you must move one letter from the word on the left to the word on the right to make two new words. You are only allowed to move one letter and must not re-arrange any of the other letters.

Example: PAIR   ART   [Air]   [Part]

25. PEAR   OAR   [   ]   [   ]

26. PRINT   EACH   [   ]   [   ]

27. LOFT   RAT   [   ]   [   ]

28. BOAT   APE   [   ]   [   ]

29. NICE   DRAW   [   ]   [   ]

30. STOOP   PEN   [   ]   [   ]

PLEASE CONTINUE ON THE NEXT PAGE

In the questions below there are two sets of words. Find a word that goes equally well with both sets.

Example: [ground, soil]   [globe, world]   [earth   ]

31. [punishment, penalty]   [superior, exceptional] [   ]

32. [steady, constant]   [building, shelter]   [   ]

33. [enclosure, stall]   [ballpoint, marker]   [   ]

34. [rubbish, scrap]   [boat, vessel]   [   ]

35. [stem, twig]   [pursue, track]   [   ]

36. [booth, stand]   [stop, pause]   [   ]

In the following questions the pairs of letters are related in the same way. Use the alphabet shown below to work out the missing letters.

A B C D E F G H I J K L M N O P Q R S T U V W X Y Z

Example: CF is related to DH as XV is related to   [YX   ]

37.   RH is related to SG as PL is related to   [   ]

38.   IV is related to LW as QR is related to   [   ]

39.   EC is related to JA as UP is related to   [   ]

40.   ME is related to LE as KO is related to   [   ]

41.   KR is related to NM as GS is related to   [   ]

42.   ZZ is related to AX as CP is related to   [   ]

PLEASE CONTINUE ON THE NEXT PAGE

In the questions below find the number that continues the sequence.

Example: 3, 6, 9, 12,   [15]

43.   10, 12, 14, 16,   [   ]

44.   20, 17, 14, 11,   [   ]

45.   2, 4, 8, 16, 32,   [   ]

46.   75, 70, 65, 60,   [   ]

47.   1, 2, 3, 4, 5, 6,   [   ]

48.   3, 4, 6, 9, 13, 18,   [   ]

In the sentences below you must find a **four-letter** word that is hidden at the end of one word and the start of the next word. You must not change the order of the letters.

Example: The he<u>ro le</u>d them to safety.

49.   When did you cross the Atlantic?

50.   The car turned round that corner.

51.   The bride asked the groom something.

52.   The vicar opened the church door.

53.   The black knight always rode alone.

54.   The rabbit chewed all the flowers.

PLEASE CONTINUE ON THE NEXT PAGE

55. Dave, Jayne and Nikki catch buses to go to the same destination.

Dave catches the 10.30 am bus.

Nikki's bus journey takes twice as long as Jayne's.

Jayne's bus leaves 15 minutes before Dave and arrives at 11.00 am.

Nikki catches the 11.15 am bus.

What time does Nikki arrive at the destination?

In the following questions the underlined word has had three consecutive letters removed. These three letters make a word without being rearranged. What is the three-letter word?

Example: Lots of people go to church on <u>day</u>   [Sun   ]

56. You play ice <u>hoc</u> with sticks and a puck.   [   ]

57. The builder pushed the <u>wheelrow.</u>   [   ]

58. The cheetah chased the <u>elope</u>.   [   ]

59. The <u>spar</u> is a common garden bird.   [   ]

60. Do all birds have <u>fhers?</u>   [   ]

61. My favourite food is <u>saus</u> and mash.   [   ]

PLEASE CONTINUE ON THE NEXT PAGE

In the questions below find **two** words, one from each group, that are **similar** in meaning.

Example: [high, warm, fold]   [tall, pest, bright]

62.   [new, went, shabby]   [tatty, brave, foolish]

63.   [gusty, stop, brisk]   [slow, windy, dusty]

64.   [spy, park, mend]   [never, repair, worry]

65.   [sting, glue, dare]   [aim, paste, folded]

66.   [tasty, squash, wide]   [dive, clean, broad]

67.   [dense, separate, love]   [thick, tie, ruin]

In the following questions some of the words have been written in code. In each question the code has been "broken" for one word. You must use the same code to work out the second word.

A B C D E F G H I J K L M N O P Q R S T U V W X Y Z

Example: If GBTU means FAST, what does CBDL mean? [BACK   ]

68.   If NPMF means MOLE,
      what does QPTU mean?   [   ]

69.   If QNSZ is the code for ROTA,
      what is the code for ANTS?   [   ]

70.   If ORVW means LOST,
      what does SLHU mean?   [   ]

71.   If XQTQ is the code for WORM,
      what is the code for BARK?   [   ]

72.   If CKPV means BLOW,
      what does SDTS mean?   [   ]

73.   If RIGS is the code for PEAK,
      what is the code for HAIR?   [   ]

PLEASE CONTINUE ON THE NEXT PAGE

In these questions there are two groups of words. The word in the left-hand brackets has been formed in a certain way using letters from the other words on the left-hand side. Use the letters in the words on the right-hand side to form a word **in the same way**.

Example: CART [TEST] BEST : BARN [NOON] SOON

74. PARK [PAST] LOST : COAT [   ] FOLD

75. MOVE [VOLE] LEAD : MARK [   ] INCH

76. CREW [WENT] NEST : CROP [   ] SLAT

77. TASTE [STEP] PRIZE : SLOPE [   ] NUDGE

78. WILD [DEAL] EATS : MIST [   ] APEX

79. PACE [PALM] LOOM : FADE [   ] ROOM

80. Kitty, Tony and Manuel need £5 each to buy a train ticket.

Kitty has £4.25.

Tony and Manuel both have more money than Kitty.

Which one of the following must be true?

A. Manuel has more money than Tony.

B. Kitty doesn't buy a train ticket.

C. Kitty borrows some money from Manuel and Tony so that she can buy a train ticket.

D. Kitty, Tony and Manuel all buy train tickets.

E. Tony and Manuel have enough money to each buy a train ticket.

THIS IS THE END OF THE TEST

Practice Paper 12

(Verbal Reasoning)

Please read the following before you start the Practice Paper:

1. Do not begin the Practice Paper until you are told to do so.

2. The Practice Paper contains 80 questions and you have 50 minutes to complete it.

3. Read the questions carefully so that you know what to do.

4. Mark your answers clearly using a <u>pencil</u>.

5. If you want to change one of your answers, rub out the wrong answer completely and enter the new answer. <u>Do not cross out any answers</u>.

6. Try and answer as many questions as you can. You may not be able to answer all of them, so if you cannot answer a question go on to the next one. Do not spend too much time on one question.

7. When you get to the end of the Practice Paper, go back and check your answers.

In the following questions some of the words have been written in code. In each question the code has been "broken" for one word. You must use the same code to work out the second word.

A B C D E F G H I J K L M N O P Q R S T U V W X Y Z

Example: If XIFO means WHEN, what does UBNF mean? [TAME   ]

1. If ANVK means BOWL,
    what does BNKC mean?   [   ]

2. If EFDE is the code for HIGH,
    what is the code for CHEW?   [   ]

3. If FGPV means DENT,
    what does ETQY mean?   [   ]

4. If CKWI is the code for BITE,
    what is the code for MOVE?   [   ]

5. If NNMF means PLOD,
    what does UCJM mean?   [   ]

6. If DGPF is the code for BEND,
    what is the code for HARE?   [   ]

In the questions below find **two** words, one from each group, that are **opposite** in meaning.

Example: [ancient, sad, best]   [angry, lift, modern]

7.   [rare, bring, loud]   [common, spoil, card]

8.   [tired, least, joy]   [wide, angry, most]

9.   [arid, never, mild]   [always, dry, spare]

10. [first, hurry, pull]   [last, great, low]

11. [shrink, prove, tidy]   [disorderly, support, lessen]

12. [hasten, create, barter]   [begin, delay, starve]

PLEASE CONTINUE ON THE NEXT PAGE

In the following questions the underlined word has had three consecutive letters removed. These three letters make a word without being rearranged. What is the three-letter word?

Example: The <u>tain</u> sailed the ship into the harbour. [cap   ]

13. He searched the internet using his <u>comer</u>. [   ]

14. The rats <u>foled</u> the Pied Piper. [   ]

15. He bought some old paintings and other <u>iques</u>. [   ]

16. The <u>don</u> is a mythical fire-breathing monster. [   ]

17. The skydiver jumped from the plane with his <u>parace</u>. [   ]

18. Let's have tea and cucumber <u>swiches</u>. [   ]

19. Dietmar, Andre and Kevin need £8.50 each to buy the latest spy novel.

Kevin has £8.49.

Dietmar and Andre both have more money than Kevin.

Which one of the following must be true?

A. Dietmar has more money than Andre.

B. Andre doesn't buy the spy novel.

C. Dietmar, Andre and Kevin all buy the spy novel.

D. No-one buys the spy novel.

E. Dietmar and Andre have enough money to buy the spy novel.

PLEASE CONTINUE ON THE NEXT PAGE

In the questions below find the number that continues the sequence.

Example: 5, 10, 15, 20,   [25]

20. 9, 12, 15, 18,   [   ]

21. 19, 17, 15, 13, 11,   [   ]

22. 80, 40, 20, 10,   [   ]

23. 21, 20, 18, 15, 11,   [   ]

24. 2, 6, 10, 14,   [   ]

25. 9, 0, 10, 1, 11, 2,   [   ]

In the sentences below you must find a **four-letter** word that is hidden at the end of one word and the start of the next word. You must not change the order of the letters.

Example: Whe<u>re ar</u>e my new running shoes?

26. The creaky door opened very slowly.

27. A student asked the teacher questions.

28. What should we do later tonight?

29. The witch and her cat flew.

30. Did the doctor examine your leg?

31. They went to the restaurant today.

PLEASE CONTINUE ON THE NEXT PAGE

In these questions find **two** words, one from each group, which make a new word when combined. The word from the group on the left must come first.

Example: [car, wish, pole]   [pet, tip, jet]

32. [start, rest, fix]   [dare, led, bun]

33. [bought, for, name]   [bull, tune, rest]

34. [help, ton, bar]   [king, den, fish]

35. [pull, dark, ant]   [hit, hem, hiss]

36. [spar, flop, lost]   [tan, delve, net]

37. [beak, air, spot]   [craft, not, drip]

---

38. Bill, Joanne and Claire cycle to the beach.

    Bill leaves at 7.30 am.

    Joanne leaves at 8.30 am.

    Joanne's cycle ride is three times as long as Claire's.

    Claire leaves 30 minutes before Bill and arrives at 8.00 am.

    What time does Joanne arrive at the beach?

PLEASE CONTINUE ON THE NEXT PAGE

In the following questions the pairs of letters are related in the same way. Use the alphabet shown below to work out the missing letters.

A B C D E F G H I J K L M N O P Q R S T U V W X Y Z

Example: JA is related to KB as LX is related to   [MY   ]

39.   MA is related to OD as XS is related to   [   ]

40.   TV is related to US as ML is related to   [   ]

41.   RU is related to WR as CL is related to   [   ]

42.   JE is related to EE as UR is related to   [   ]

43.   AD is related to YL as ZR is related to   [   ]

44.   MM is related to NL as DC is related to   [   ]

In the questions below you must move one letter from the word on the left to the word on the right to make two new words. You are only allowed to move one letter and must not re-arrange any of the other letters.

Example: DATE   ICE   [Ate   ]   [Dice   ]

45.   PIER   ACE   [   ]   [   ]

46.   GRIP   BARE   [   ]   [   ]

47.   DARK   EAR   [   ]   [   ]

48.   GATE   RIP   [   ]   [   ]

49.   BLOWN   PATS   [   ]   [   ]

50.   SEIZE   VENT   [   ]   [   ]

PLEASE CONTINUE ON THE NEXT PAGE

In the following questions numbers have been replaced with letters. You need to work out the answers to the sums.

Example: If A = 1, B = 2, C = 3 and D = 4. Calculate the answer to this sum **as a number:**

A + B + C = [6]

51. If A = 1, B = 2, C = 3 and D = 4

Calculate the answer to this sum **as a number:**

A + B + C + D = [   ]

52. If A = 6, B = 4, C = 2 and D = 0

Calculate the answer to this sum **as a letter:**

A - B + C = [   ]

53. If A = 0, B = 1, C = 2 and D = 3

Calculate the answer to this sum **as a letter:**

A x C x B = [   ]

54. If A = 10, B = 5, C = 2 and D = 1

Calculate the answer to this sum **as a number:**

A - C + B = [   ]

55. If A = 3, B = 6, C = 9 and D = 12

Calculate the answer to this sum **as a letter:**

A - B + C = [   ]

56. If A = 20, B = 5, C = 10 and D = 15

Calculate the answer to this sum **as a letter:**

A - C + D - B = [   ]

PLEASE CONTINUE ON THE NEXT PAGE

Using the alphabet shown below identify the next letters in the sequences.

A B C D E F G H I J K L M N O P Q R S T U V W X Y Z

Example: AC,   BD,   CE,   DF,   [EG]

57.   CM,   DL,   EK,   FJ,   [   ]

58.   LD,   JA,   HX,   FU,   [   ]

59.   GC,   LE,   QG,   VI,   [   ]

60.   KV,   LU,   JS,   MP,   IL,   [   ]

61.   AY,   BW,   DU,   GS,   KQ,   [   ]

62.   NN,   PO,   RQ,   TU,   VC,   [   ]

In these questions find one word from each pair of brackets that will complete the sentence in the most sensible way.

Example: Old is to [rice, rugged, new] as bright is to [dim, chew, spill].

63.   Exit is to [enter, show, caring] as wet is to [soaked, wear, dry].

64.   Poem is to [just, grand, poet] as novel is to [new, author, rare].

65.   Great is to [huge, grate, Britain] as nose is to [knows, smell, faces].

66.   Pilot is to [aircraft, fly, travel] as driver is to [train, bicycle, ship].

67.   Gaggle is to [goose, goat, bird] as shoal is to [fish, rabbit, swan].

68.   First is to [last, race, thirst] as quiet is to [silent, hushed, noisy].

PLEASE CONTINUE ON THE NEXT PAGE

In the questions below find a letter that goes at the end of one word and the start of the other. The **same** letter must fit in both sets of brackets.

Example: tar [t] alk   car [t] eal

69.   wis [   ] alf   fis [   ] eal

70.   bea [   ] ing   fol [   ] night

71.   tepi [   ] eck   fee [   ] ark

72.   spoi [   ] ead   shel [   ] orry

73.   chai [   ] ead   floo [   ] eady

74.   nea [   ] ask   brigh [   ] ango

In these questions the three numbers in each group are related in exactly the same way. Calculate the number to complete the third group.

Example: (1 [4] 3)   (2 [7] 5)   (1 [6] 5)

75. (1 [9] 10)   (1 [2] 3)   (3 [   ] 9)

76. (2 [16] 8)   (9 [27] 3)   (3 [   ] 4)

77. (3 [10] 7)   (9 [13] 4)   (8 [   ] 8)

78. (12 [3] 4)   (15 [5] 3)   (25 [   ] 5)

79. (18 [22] 2)   (17 [20] 1)   (4 [   ] 7)

80. (13 [10] 3)   (17 [21] 10)   (20 [   ] 7)

THIS IS THE END OF THE TEST

Answers to Practice Paper 9

1	The robber	28	4	55	MO
2	same shop.	29	30	56	n
3	guest arrived	30	D	57	t
4	door open.	31	5336	58	h
5	When should	32	1263	59	g
6	fish and	33	RARE	60	r
7	OLD & SCARF	34	5674	61	f
8	RICE & PART	35	PROD	62	2
9	ARC & HEAR	36	1253	63	2
10	OTHER & TRAMP	37	rid	64	10
11	GOT & ROAD	38	her	65	7
12	BROW & NEAT	39	art	66	0
13	destroy & break	40	row	67	16
14	exit & leave	41	can	68	15
15	timid & shy	42	rat	69	1
16	buy & purchase	43	C	70	5
17	fast & quick	44	MUST	71	8
18	wet & soaked	45	KNRS	72	11
19	star-ring	46	KNOT	73	12
20	tar-get	47	SQLM	74	HEAD
21	deter-mine	48	COLD	75	ARCH
22	grate-fully	49	QLVB	76	SOUP
23	bar-row	50	MK	77	FARM
24	stop-ping	51	JL	78	BEAD
25	10	52	VB	79	RAMP
26	D	53	PP	80	Martin
27	B	54	PJ		

Answers to Practice Paper 10

1	well	28	paper & envelope	55	20
2	bright	29	television & radio	56	D
3	mine	30	ancient & old	57	Sat
4	box	31	C	58	ice
5	spring	32	13	59	lit
6	band	33	5	60	own
7	tame & new	34	18	61	let
8	right & pail	35	4	62	cab
9	France & Germany	36	10	63	32
10	circus & kitchen	37	12	64	10
11	highest & fastest	38	bright & dull	65	21
12	fly & see	39	late & punctual	66	48
13	SC	40	fastest & slowest	67	8
14	RJ	41	commence & complete	68	9
15	GR	42	help & hinder	69	not answer
16	IV	43	cheap & expensive	70	They escaped
17	LG	44	Dave	71	coach allowed
18	GO	45	p	72	She ate
19	car	46	t	73	follow after
20	all	47	t	74	What shall
21	sun	48	n	75	rub-bed
22	pie	49	e	76	slip-per
23	den	50	d	77	has-ten
24	old	51	13	78	mar-row
25	bull & drake	52	A	79	woo-den
26	grape & raspberry	53	16	80	shop-ping
27	road & garden	54	B		

Answers to Practice Paper 11

#	Answer	#	Answer	#	Answer
1	bow-led	28	BOA & TAPE	55	12.45 pm
2	bet-ting	29	ICE & DRAWN	56	key
3	cart-ridge	30	STOP & OPEN	57	bar
4	win-king	31	fine	58	ant
5	pea-cock	32	stable	59	row
6	pull-over	33	pen	60	eat
7	3465	34	junk	61	age
8	5441	35	stalk	62	shabby & tatty
9	RARE	36	stall	63	gusty & windy
10	2462	37	QK	64	mend & repair
11	BARK	38	TS	65	glue & paste
12	25462	39	ZN	66	wide & broad
13	8	40	JO	67	dense & thick
14	C	41	JN	68	POST
15	12	42	DN	69	ZMSR
16	B	43	18	70	PIER
17	6	44	8	71	CCTO
18	150	45	64	72	REST
19	e	46	55	73	JEOZ
20	r	47	7	74	COLD
21	p	48	24	75	RAIN
22	k	49	the Atlantic	76	POST
23	t	50	car turned	77	OPEN
24	m	51	bride asked	78	TAPS
25	PEA & ROAR	52	vicar opened	79	FARM
26	PINT & REACH	53	rode alone	80	B
27	LOT & RAFT	54	rabbit chewed		

Answers to Practice Paper 12

1	COLD	28	What should	55	B
2	ZEBT	29	witch and	56	A
3	CROW	30	doctor examine	57	GI
4	NQYI	31	the restaurant	58	DR
5	WALK	32	start-led	59	AK
6	JCTG	33	for-tune	60	NG
7	rare & common	34	bar-king	61	PO
8	least & most	35	ant-hem	62	XS
9	never & always	36	spar-tan	63	enter & dry
10	first & last	37	air-craft	64	poet & author
11	tidy & disorderly	38	11.30 am	65	grate & knows
12	hasten & delay	39	ZV	66	aircraft & train
13	put	40	NI	67	goose & fish
14	low	41	HI	68	last & noisy
15	ant	42	PR	69	h
16	rag	43	XZ	70	k
17	hut	44	EB	71	d
18	and	45	PIE & RACE	72	l
19	E	46	RIP & BARGE	73	r
20	21	47	ARK & DEAR	74	t
21	9	48	ATE & GRIP	75	6
22	5	49	BLOW & PANTS	76	12
23	6	50	SIZE & EVENT	77	16
24	18	51	10	78	5
25	12	52	B	79	13
26	door opened	53	A	80	21
27	student asked	54	13		

Progress Record

Practice Paper 9

Date completed: ....

Page	1	2	3	4	5	6	7	8	Total
Possible	12	12	6	12	7	12	12	7	80
Score									

Practice Paper 10

Date completed: ....

Page	1	2	3	4	5	6	7	8	Total
Possible	12	12	7	12	7	6	12	12	80
Score									

Practice Paper 11

Date completed: ....

Page	1	2	3	4	5	6	7	8	Total
Possible	12	6	12	12	12	7	12	7	80
Score									

Practice Paper 12

Date completed: ....

Page	1	2	3	4	5	6	7	8	Total
Possible	12	7	12	7	12	6	12	12	80
Score									